FROG ON A LOG?

SPORTS

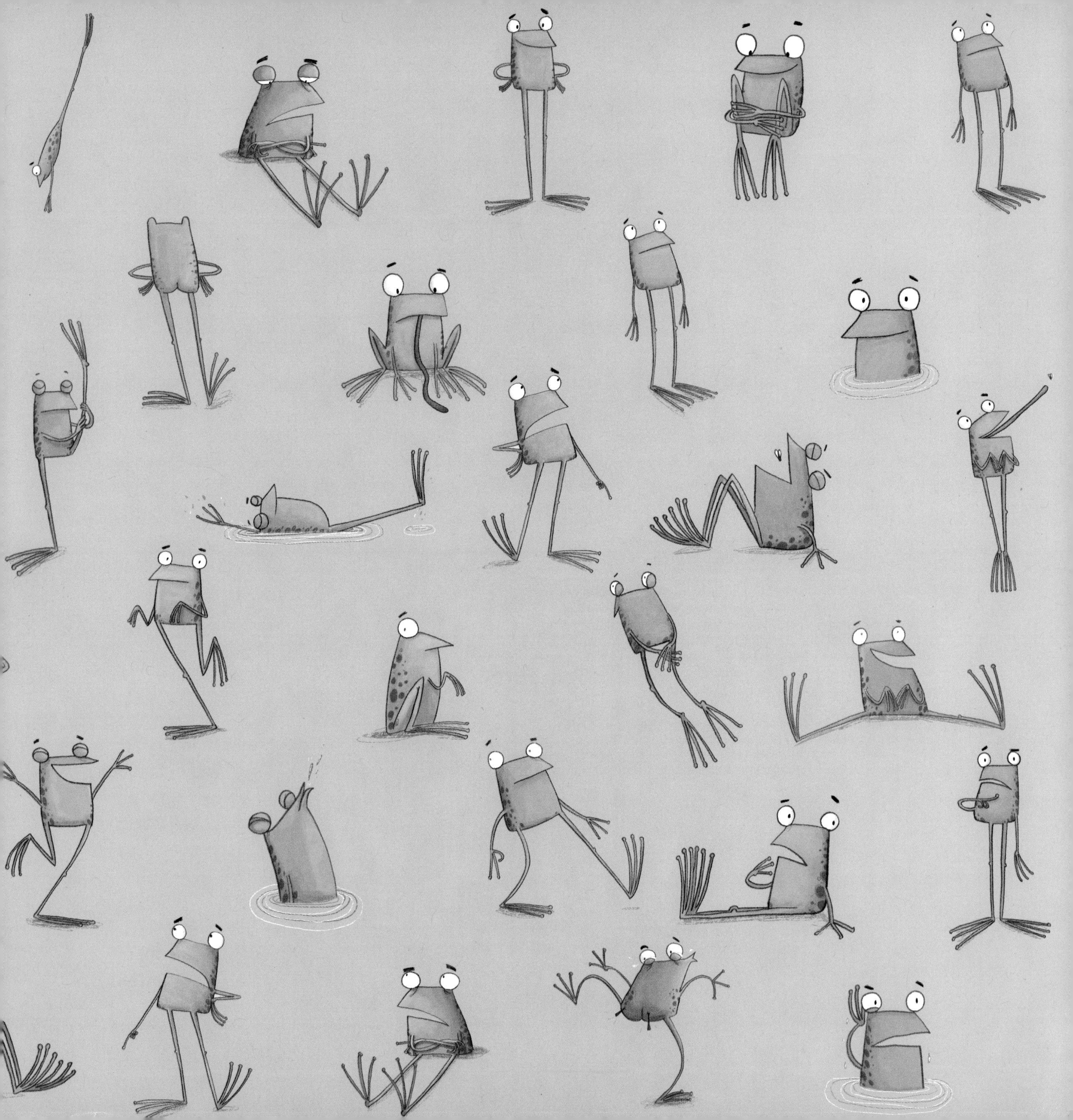

Frog on a Log? was originally published in the UK by Hodder Children's Books, a division of Hachette Children's Books, under the title *Oi Frog!*

ISBN 978-0-545-86495-4

12 11 10 9 8 7 6 5 4 3 2 1 16 17 18 19 20 21

Printed in the U.S.A. 40

First Scholastic paperback printing, January 2016

The text type was set in Coventry ITC Medium.
The display type was set in Hot Coffee.

To Linda,
without whom
a very small part of
this book would not
have been possible!
— K.G.

In loving
memory of
Joan and Ian
— J.F.

FROG ON A LOG?

Kes Gray
and Jim Field

SCHOLASTIC INC.

"Sit on a log!"
said the cat.

"But I don't want to sit on a log," said the frog.
"Logs are all hard and uncomfortable.
And they can give you splinters. Ouch!"

"I don't care," said the cat.
"You're a **frog**, so you must sit on a **log**."

"Can't I sit on a mat?" asked the frog.

"Only **cats** sit on **mats**," said the cat.

"What about a chair?" said the frog.
"I wouldn't mind
sitting on a chair."

"**Hares**
sit on **chairs**,"
said the cat.

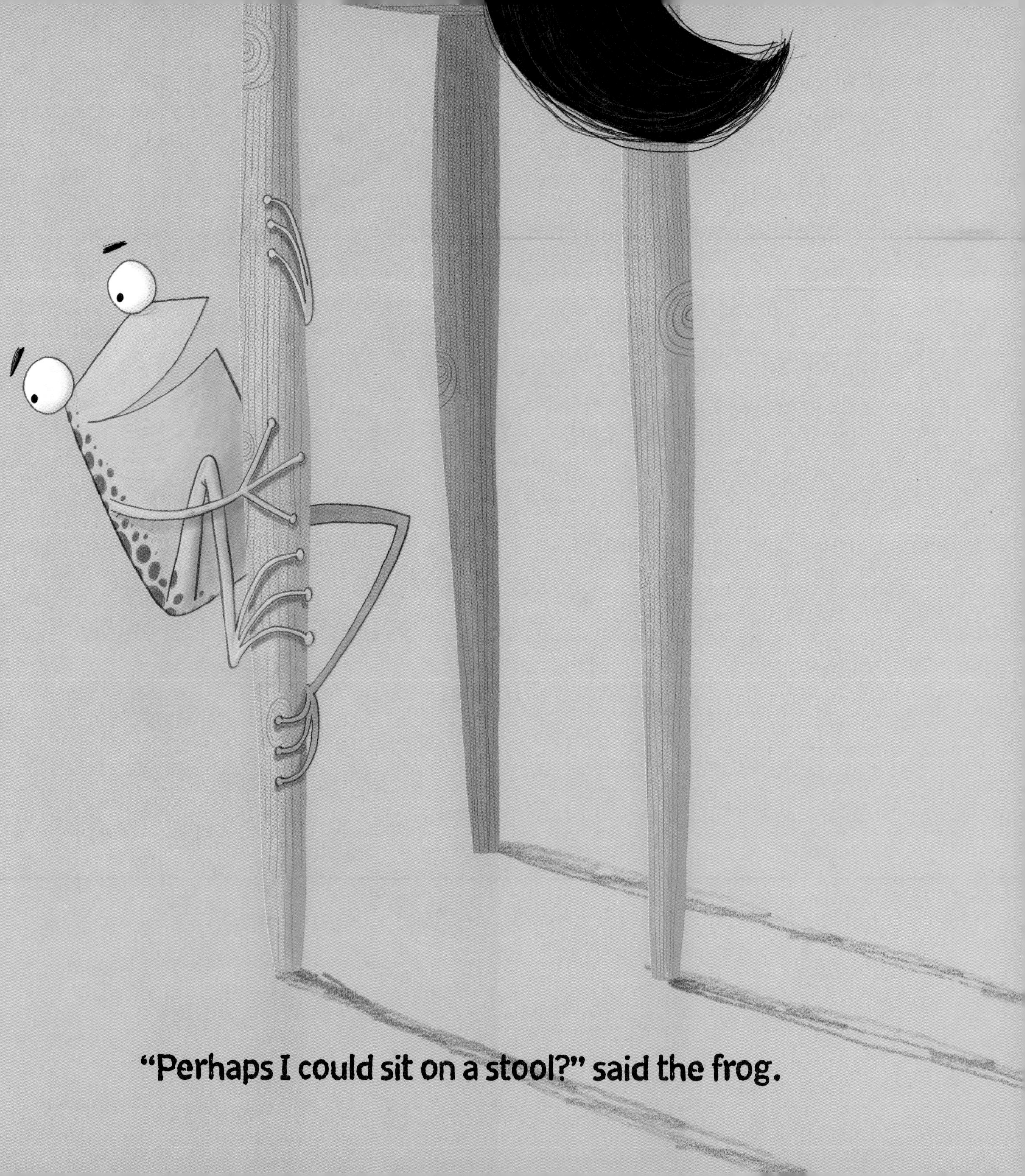

“Perhaps I could sit on a stool?” said the frog.

"**Mules**
sit on **stools**,"
said the cat.

"What about a sofa?" said the frog.
"I could stretch right out on a sofa!"

"**Gophers** sit on **sofas**," said the cat.

"It's very simple, really."

“Cats
sit on mats,
hares
sit on chairs,
mules
sit on stools,
gophers
sit on sofas,
and frogs
sit on logs.”

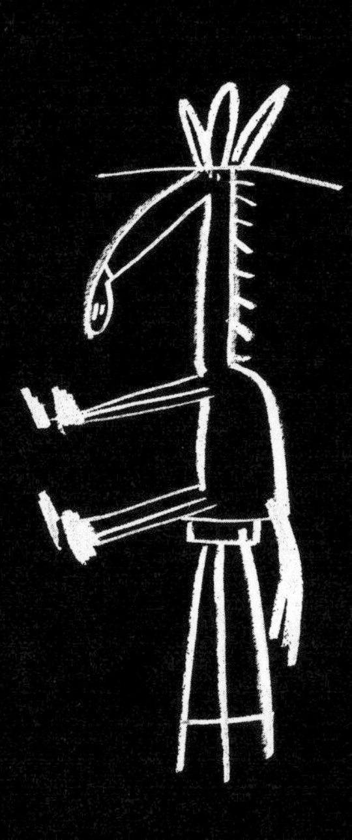

"What do lions sit on?"
asked the frog.

"Lions
sit on **irons**,"
said the cat.

"Ouch!" said the frog.
"What do parrots sit on?"

"Parrots
sit on carrots,"
said the cat.

"Lions
sit on
irons,
and
parrots
sit on
carrots."

"That doesn't sound very comfortable," said the frog.

"It's not about being comfortable," said the cat.

"It's about doing the right thing."

"What do foxes sit on?" asked the frog.

"Foxes
sit on **boxes**,"
said the cat.

"Foxes
sit on **boxes**,
and **fleas**
sit on **peas**."

"What do goats sit on?" asked the frog.

"Goats
sit on coats,"
said the cat.

"Goats
sit on coats,
cows
sit on plows,
and storks
sit on forks."

38

"What do gorillas sit on?"
asked the frog.

"Gorillas
sit on
pillars,"
said the cat.

"Gorillas
sit on pillars,
rats
sit on hats,
weasels
sit on
easels,
and moles
sit on
poles."

"What do seals sit on?" asked the frog.

"Don't you know anything?"
said the cat.

"Seals
sit on wheels,
doves
sit on gloves,
newts
sit on flutes,
lizards
sit on wizards,
and apes
sit on grapes."

"What about puffins?" asked the frog.

"Puffins
sit on muffins,"
said the cat.

"Puffins
sit on muffins,
snakes
sit on cakes,
owls
sit on towels,

gibbons
sit on ribbons,
lambs
sit on jams,
and bees
sit on keys."

"Well, I never knew that," said the frog.

"Well, you do now," said the cat.

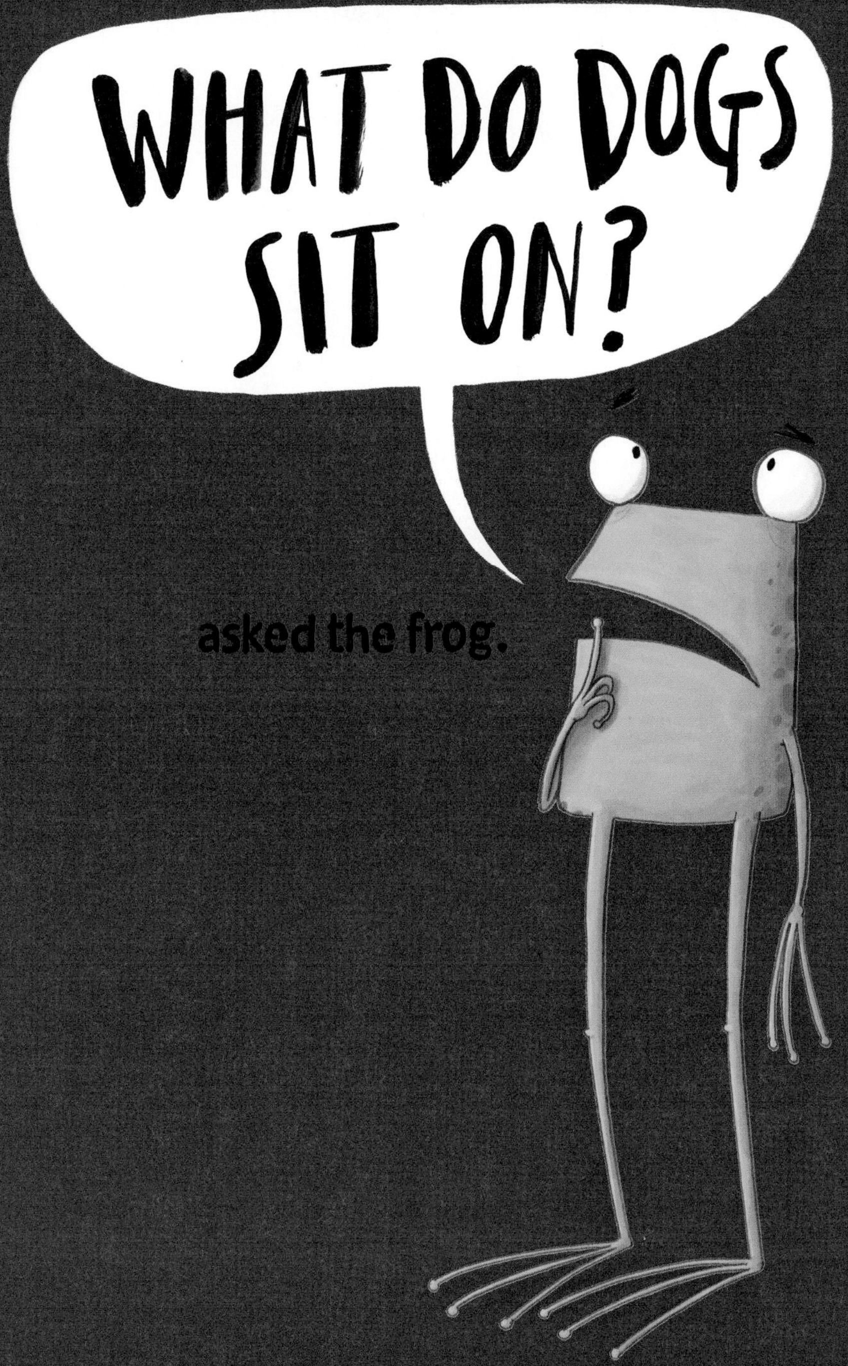

WHAT DO DOGS SIT ON?

asked the frog.

"I was hoping
you weren't
going to ask that,"
said the cat . . .

HELP!

SPORTS

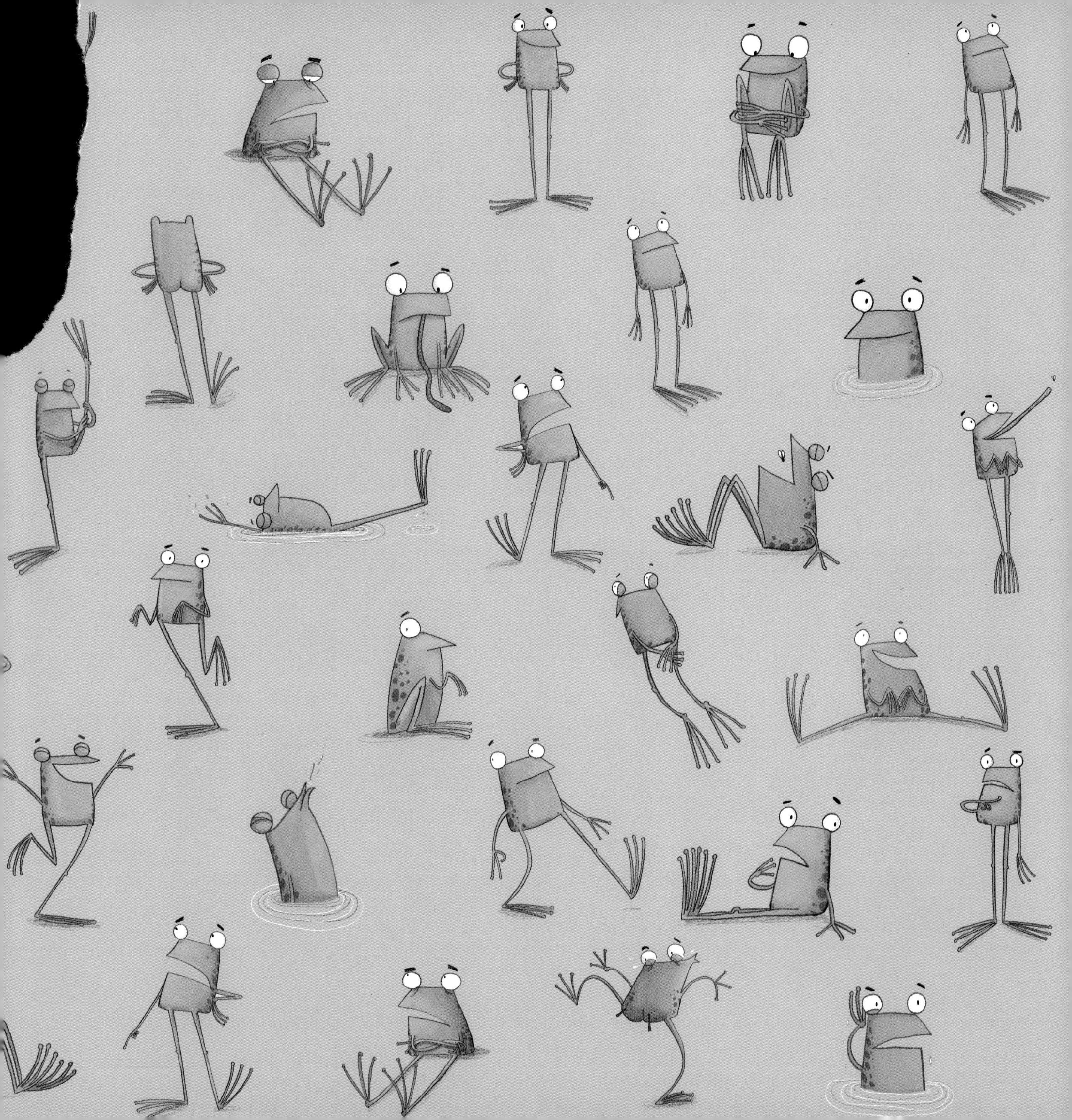